Mathematics 1

CW00842759

Fill in the missing numbers.

a | 1 | | 3 | | | 6 | 7 | | | 10 | | 12 |

b | | 2 | 3 | | 5 | | | 8 | 9 | | 11 | |

c | 1 | 2 | | 4 | | | 7 | | | 10 | | 12 |

Write the answers in the box.

d (5p) + (1p) (2p) = [ ] p   **e** (20p) + (5p) (1p) = [ ] p

f (10p) − (2p) (5p) = [ ] p   **g** (5p) (10p) (1p) − (2p) = [ ] p

What time is it?

h [ ] o'clock   **i** [ ] o'clock

j [ ] o'clock   **k** [ ] o'clock

Write the answer in the box.

l add 4 and 7 [ ]   **m** take 3 from 10 [ ]

n 17 is 10 more than [ ]   **o** the difference betweeen 12 and 5 is [ ]

p the total of 5 and 9 is [ ]   **q** the sum of 6 and 7 is [ ]

Write the letters in each group in alphabetical order.

a F X T B L O _____

b N Y J E R Z _____

c P A U S C M _____

d G U K I E Q _____

e V O H N A S _____

Write the correct word from the list under each picture.

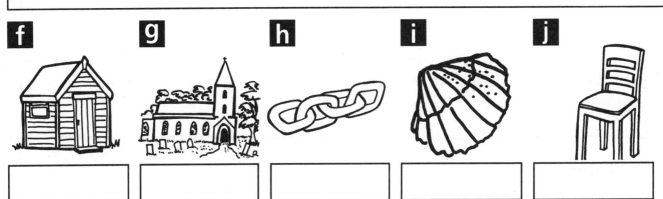

| church | chair | shed | shell | chain |

f **g** **h** **i** **j**

The words below the pictures need a first and a last letter.
Write in the missing letters.

k _ a _   **l** _ oo _   **m** _ on _   **n** _ ir _

o _ re _   **p** _ la _   **q** _ ea _   **r** _ oa _

Living things need air, food and water. Living things grow.

a Look at the picture. Colour the living things red.

In the box below are the names of things in the picture.
Underline the names of the living things.

boat	water	bird	fish	grass	girl	boy
horse	fence	sheep	tree	church	tractor	

b Look at the pictures below.

Some are living things. Some are not living things.
Colour the living things red.

plant	chair	balloons	dog	television

snake	rocket	frog	baby	rose

Write one list of the living things.
Write another list of the things that are not living.

Living things: _____ _____ _____

_____ _____ _____

Things not living: _____ _____

_____ _____

Writing 1

Write these sentences correctly.
Begin each sentence with a capital letter.
End each sentence with a full stop.

a children are playing in the park

_____

b a girl and a boy are on the see-saw

_____

c three children are riding on the spaceship

_____

d others are waiting to climb the ladder

_____

e they want to use the slide

_____

f a small boy is kicking a ball

_____

g grown-ups are sitting on a bench

_____

h one has a dog on a lead

_____

Which picture in each row is the odd one out?
Write the number of the picture.

a   1   2   3   4

The odd one out is ☐

b   1   2   3   4

The odd one out is ☐

Fill in the missing numbers.

c 1 2 3 ___ 5 ___   **d** 9 8 7 ___ 5 ___

e 1 ___ ___ 4 5 6   **f** 6 5 ___ 3 ___ 1

g 2 4 6 ___ 10 ___   **h** 1 3 5 ___ 9 ___

These pictures are in the wrong order.
Write the numbers of the pictures in their correct order.

i   1   2   3

☐   ☐   ☐

Reading and Vocabulary 2

Read this passage carefully.

The swan is one of our most beautiful birds. On the water and in the air it is the fastest of our water birds. The swan feeds on water plants.

Male swans are called cobs. The females are called pens. A pair of swans mate for life. The pen lays about six eggs on a heap of plant matter. The pen sits on the eggs, while the cob keeps close guard.

The young, called cygnets, are born with short necks. They are covered with thick down. The cygnets can run and swim just a few hours after hatching. The parents look after them for several months.

Read the questions carefully.
Write your answer on the line after the question.

a Can swans fly faster than any other water birds?_____

b What do swans eat?_____

c What do we call female swans?_____

d What are young swans called?_____

e When the cygnets are born,
   what covering is on their bodies? _____

f For how long do the parents look after their cygnets?_____

Write out these sentences. Replace the underlined words with one of the words in the box.

generous	pest	damp	lonely	dash

g Do not wear clothes that are <u>slightly wet</u>._____

h Vera had to <u>run quickly</u> to catch the bus. _____

i My dad is <u>not mean</u> with his money._____

j David was <u>without friends</u> but he would not play out._____

k The rat is a <u>harmful animal</u>._____

Mathematics 2

How many tens

a in 20 ? ⬚   **b** in 40 ? ⬚   **c** in 70 ? ⬚

d in 50 ? ⬚   **e** in 80 ? ⬚   **f** in 10 ? ⬚

g in 30 ? ⬚   **h** in 90 ? ⬚   **i** in 60 ? ⬚

What time is it?

j ⬚   **k** ⬚

l The twelve months of the year below are in the wrong order. Write them in their correct order.

June, March, November, February, May, April, September, July, January, August, December, October

1 _____   2 _____   3 _____

4 _____   5 _____   6 _____

7 _____   8 _____   9 _____

10 _____   11 _____   12 _____

Write the answer in the box.

m subtract 8 from 13 ⬚   **n** 30 divided by 10 is ⬚

o 5 less than 18 is ⬚   **p** 17 minus 6 is ⬚

q the difference between 11 and 4 is ⬚   **r** the total of 6 and 17 is ⬚

Put in the missing letters in alphabetical order.

a k l __ __ o __ __ r __ __ u __

b c __ __ f __ h i __ __ l __ n

c o __ __ r s __ u __ __ x __ z

d h i __ __ __ m n __ __ q __ s

e a __ __ d __ f __ __ i __ k __

---

a, e, i, o and u are vowels.
Complete the word under each picture by writing a vowel on the line.

f  **g**  **h**  **i**  **j**

| b _ n | m _ g | c _ t | d _ g | n _ t |

Each word should begin with br or pr.
Complete each word by writing br or pr on the line.

k  **l**  **m**  **n**

| ___ esent | ___ idge | ___ ide | ___ ison |

o  **p**  **q**  **r**

| ___ ize | ___ incess | ___ ooch | ___ ush |

Science 2

Use words from the list below to complete the sentences.
Each word may be used more than once.

die	water	back	hot	hungry
need	air	withered	rain	breathes

The girl is swimming.

a Her head is above the _____ .

b She needs to breathe _____ .

c Without _____ she would drown.

The diver is in the sea.

d The diver needs _____ .

e The _____ he needs is in a pack
on his _____ .

f He _____ the _____ through
a tube.

The man is lost in a desert.

g It is very _____ .

h The man needs _____ .

i If he cannot find _____ he will
_____ .

There has been no rain for months.

j The plants are _____ .

k They _____ water.

l The people will be _____ if it does
not _____ .

Write these sentences correctly.

a it is a fine day for the beach

_____

b the sun is shining

_____

c the sea is calm

_____

d two girls are paddling in the sea

_____

e one boy has made a sandcastle

_____

f he put a flag on top

_____

g some children are playing cricket

_____

h a woman is eating an ice-cream

_____

Thinking 2

Two of the squares in each row are blank.
Fill in the two blanks to complete the pattern.

a

b

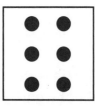  

---

c Write in the values of the blank coins.

What do the people in the top row of pictures use from the second row of pictures? Finish the sentences.

| gardener | cook | nurse | fireman |

| thermometer | ladder | fork | spoon |

d The gardener uses a _____ .

e The _____ uses a spoon.

f The nurse uses a _____ .

g The _____ uses a _____ .

Reading and Vocabulary 3

The body of an earthworm is made of many rings. These rings are called segments. The earthworm grows to about 25 centimetres. It may have as many as 150 segments.

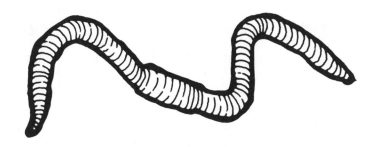

Earthworms cannot see or hear. But they are aware of light and movement. They like to live in soil which is moist. Most of their food consists of dead plants. As they eat, they also take in some soil, sand and pebbles.

The earthworm helps gardeners and farmers. As earthworms burrow, they draw dead plants and air into the soil. There the dead plants rot quickly. This improves the soil for growing new plants.

Read each sentence carefully.
Write 'T' if the sentence is true.
Write 'F' if the sentence is false.

a Earthworms can see.

b Each ring in an earthworm's body is called a segment.

c The earthworm grows to about 150 centimetres.

d Moist soil is a good home for earthworms.

e Earthworms burrow in the soil.

f The earthworm helps the gardener.

Write the correct name under each picture.

g   **h**   **i**   **j**   **k**

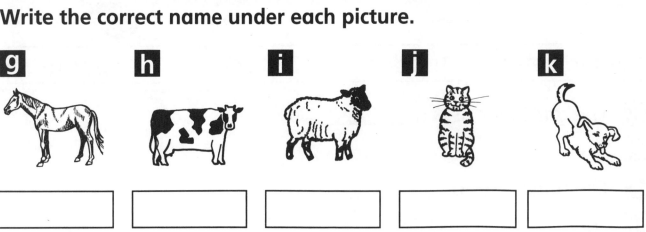

HOMEWORK BOOK 1 ANSWERS

Note for users

Taking an interest in the child's work is of great importance. Take every opportunity to praise work that is correct, and offer help and advice where the child experiences difficulty. Make sure that the child understands the instructions which introduce each exercise. Some children experience more difficulty with the instructions than with the work itself.

There are advantages in allowing the child to mark his or her own work. This informs the child of the correct answer in cases where mistakes have occurred. It is important to look again at answers that are wrong and for the child to discover why an answer is incorrect so that he or she can learn as a result of the error.

Where a weakness is revealed, further similar exercises can be provided to give the child more practice and confidence.

A child should not be expected to undertake too much work in a short time. The exercises should be well spaced out so that the last pages are being worked towards the end of the appropriate school year.

Reading and Vocabulary 1

a F	b T	c T
d F	e T	f F

 Mathematics 1

a 2, 4, 5, 8, 9, 11   b 1, 4, 6, 7, 10, 12
c 3, 5, 6, 8, 9, 11
d 8p   e 26p
f 3p   g 14p
h four o'clock   i nine o'clock
j seven o'clock   k one o'clock
l 11   m 7
n 7   o 7
p 14   q 13

 Language Skills 1

a B F L O T X   b E J N R Y Z
c A C M P S U   d E G I K Q U
e A H N O S V   f shed
g church   h chain   i shell
j chair   k cap   l book
m pond   n fire   o tree
p flag   q head   r soap

 Science 1

a bird   fish   grass   girl   boy
   horse   sheep   tree

b <u>Living things</u>   <u>Things not living</u>
   plant   chair
   dog   balloons
   snake   television
   frog   rocket
   baby
   rose

 Writing 1

a Children are playing in the park.
b A girl and a boy are on the see-saw.
c Three children are riding on the spaceship.
d Others are waiting to climb the ladder.
e They want to use the slide.
f A small boy is kicking a ball.
g Grown-ups are sitting on a bench.
h One has a dog on a lead.

Thinking 1

a 3	b 2	c 4, 6
d 6, 4	e 2, 3	f 4, 2
g 8, 12	h 7, 11	i 3 1 2

 Reading and Vocabulary 2

a yes   b water plants
c pens   d cygnets
e thick down   f several months
g damp   h dash
i generous   j lonely
k pest

Mathematics 2

a 2	b 4	c 7
d 5	e 8	f 1
g 3	h 9	i 6
j half-past ten	k half-past two	

l   1 January   2 February   3 March
    4 April   5 May   6 June
    7 July   8 August   9 September
    10 October   11 November   12 December

m 5	n 3
o 13	p 11
q 7	r 23

Language Skills 2

a m n, p q, s t, v   b d e, g, j k, m
c p q, t, v w, y   d j k l, o p, r
e b c, e, g h, j, l   f bin
g mug   h cat   i dog
j net   k present   l bridge
m bride   n prison   o prize
p princess   q brooch   r brush

 Science 2

a water   b air
c air   d air
e air, back   f breathes, air
g hot   h water
i water, die   j withered
k need   l hungry, rain

Writing 2

a It is a fine day for the beach.
b The sun is shining.
c The sea is calm.
d Two girls are paddling in the sea.
e One boy has made a sandcastle.
f He put a flag on top.
g Some children are playing cricket.
h A woman is eating an ice-cream.

Thinking 2

a or similar arrangement
b or similar arrangement
c 1p, 2p, 5p, 10p, 20p, 50p, £1
d fork   e cook
f thermometer   g fireman, ladder

Reading and Vocabulary 3

a F   b T   c F
d T   e T   f T
g horse   h cow   i sheep
j cat   k dog

Mathematics 3

a 5p   b 9p   c 3p
d 22p   e 13   f 20
g 46   h 5   i 21
j 7   k 10   l 18
m 27   n 22   o 2
p 3   q 1   r 4
s 5   t 2, 8   u 4, 3
v 7, 6   w 82

Language Skills 3

a z   b a   c s
d j   e o   f nest
g sock   h mask   i plug
j fist   k fox, box   l cup, pup
m page, cage   n flower, tower

Science 3

a water   b food   c plants
d roots   e soil   f water
g leaves   h leaves   i water
j leaves   k plant

Writing 3

a The car had a puncture. The driver got out the spare wheel. He took off the wheel with the punctured tyre.

b Then the driver put on the spare wheel. The wheel with the puncture was put in the boot. The car was driven away.

Thinking 3

a 2   b 3
c ○□○□○□□   d □□□○○□□
e □○□○□□   f ○○□□□○○
g ○□□□□○□   h 3, 1, 4, 2

Reading and Vocabulary 4

a king   b boss
c nose   d exhausted
e victory   f spider's
g banana   h pear
i apple   j grapes
k lemon

Mathematics 4

a a quarter-past five or 5.15   b a quarter-to two or 1.45
c 5   d 6
e 50p   f 20p
g 31   h 31
i 30   j 31
k 30   l 30
m 12   n 16
o 10   p 14
q 12   r 15

Language Skills 4

a chair   desk   television   zoo
b apple   melon   orange   pear
c cow   donkey horse   sheep
d elf   e octopus
f axe   g icicle
h umbrella   i orange
j ambulance   k egg
l train   m draw
n truck   o trolley
p drum

Science 4

a cat   b rabbit   c spider
d sheep   e lion   f deer
g dog   h cow   i human
j giraffe
k Eat Plants Only   Eat Other Animals
   rabbit   cat
   sheep   spider
   deer   lion
   cow   dog
   giraffe   human

Writing 4

a Last Christmas we had a big family party.
b Auntie Helen came from Leeds.
c My cousins, Joe and Emma, were there.
d Uncle Melvin from Wales gave me a video.
e The video was called Robin Hood.
f Our dog Chips got a new collar.
g We all had a wonderful Christmas Day.

Thinking 4

a back and front   high and low
   large and small   wide and narrow
b 8 12   **c** 9 15
d 20   **e** 20 10
f A carpenter makes tables.
   A cow makes milk.
   A builder makes houses.
   A baker makes bread.

Reading and Vocabulary 5

a pod   **b** factory
c cleaned   **d** butter
e sugar   **f** hot
g bread   **h** jar
i tiny   **j** hill
k paper

Mathematics 5

a ⊕   **b** 1
c 1   **d** 4   **e** 2
f 13   **g** 5   **h** 12
i 19   **j** 11   **k** 3
l 9   **m** 10   **n** C E G J L
o 8   **p** 10   **q** 9
r 4   **s** 6   **t** 15
u 4   **v** 16

Mathematics 3

a The total value of the coins is 13p.

Which coin is missing? [ ] p

---

b You have    You spend 8p.

How much have you got left? [ ] p

---

c How much more do
you need to make 20p?   [ ] p

---

d You have   You are given

How much do you have now? [ ] p

---

e 3 + 10 = [ ]   **f** 10 x 2 = [ ]   **g** 33 + 13 = [ ]

h 50 ÷ 10 = [ ]   **i** 25 – 4 = [ ]   **j** 23 – 10 – 6 = [ ]

k 40 – 10 – 10 – 10 = [ ]   **l** 34 – 16 = [ ]

m 9 + 18 = [ ]   **n** 17 + 10 – 5 = [ ]

Write half of each number in the box.

o 4 [ ]   **p** 6 [ ]   **q** 2 [ ]   **r** 8 [ ]   **s** 10 [ ]

Complete these statements.

t twenty-eight is _____ tens and _____ ones

u forty-three is _____ tens and _____ ones

v seventy-six is _____ tens and _____ ones

w 8 tens and 2 ones is _____

a Which is the **last** letter in the alphabet? _____

b Which is the **first** letter? _____

c Which letter comes before **t** ? _____

d Which letter comes after **i** ? _____

e Which letter comes between **n** and **p** ? _____

a, e, i, o and **u** are vowels.

Complete the word under each picture by writing a vowel on the line.

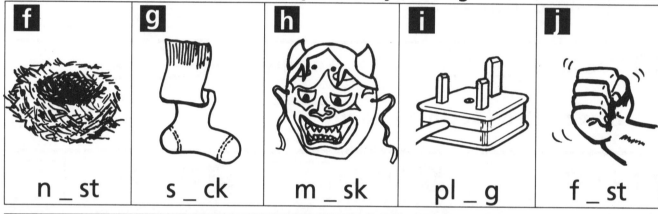

f	g	h	i	j
n _ st	s _ ck	m _ sk	pl _ g	f _ st

Words that rhyme are words that sound alike.
In each part there are three pictures with their names.
Two of the names rhyme. One does not rhyme.
On the lines write the two words that rhyme.

k
fox
shoe
box _____
_____

l
cup
pup
cap _____
_____

m
cake
page
cage _____
_____

n
flower
tower
towel _____
_____

Science 3

After each sentence there are two words.
Write the correct word in the space in the sentence.

a All living things need air, _____ and food.   **[water/milk]**

b Much of our _____ comes from plants.   **[water/food]**

c But _____ have to make their own food.   **[people/plants]**

d The _____ of the plant are in the soil.   **[roots/leaves]**

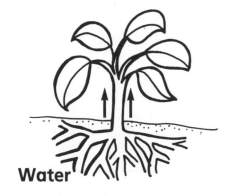

Water

e There is water in the _____.
[light/soil]

f The roots take_____ from the soil
which then goes to all parts of the
plant.   **[roots/water]**

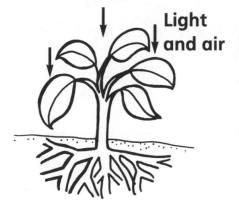

**Light
and air**

g The water helps the _____ to
spread out.   **[leaves/seeds]**

h The _____ of the plant collect
light and air.   **[roots/leaves]**

i Now the leaves have _____, light
and air.   **[water/food]**

Food

j The _____ use water, light and air
to make food.   **[roots/leaves]**

k The food goes to all parts of the
_____ .   **[plant/soil]**

page **17**

Writing 3

Put the sentences together in the right order.

a He took off the wheel with the punctured tyre.

The car had a puncture.

The driver got out the spare wheel.

_____

_____

_____

b Then the driver put on the spare wheel.

The car was driven away.

The wheel with the puncture was put in the boot.

_____

_____

_____

Thinking 3

Which picture in each row is the odd one out?
Write the number of the picture.

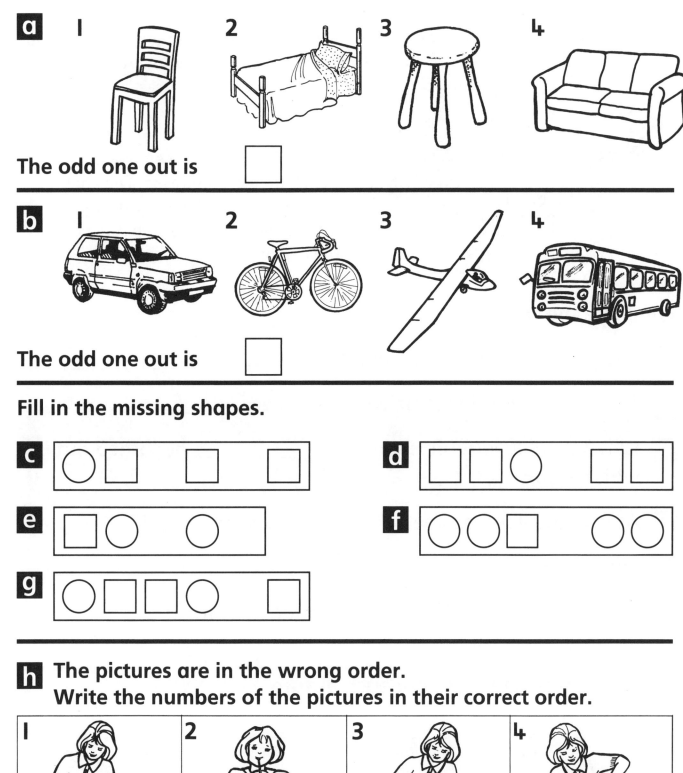

a 1 2 3 4

The odd one out is ☐

b 1 2 3 4

The odd one out is ☐

Fill in the missing shapes.

c ◯ ☐ ☐ ☐

d ☐ ☐ ◯ ☐ ☐

e ☐ ◯ ◯

f ◯ ◯ ☐ ◯ ◯

g ◯ ☐ ☐ ◯ ☐

h The pictures are in the wrong order.
Write the numbers of the pictures in their correct order.

1 2 3 4

☐ ☐ ☐ ☐

page 19

One day a tiny gnat was boasting.

He said to his friends, "The lion thinks he's king, but I'll show him who's boss."

So the gnat jumped on the lion's back, and bit him. The lion roared.

Then the gnat bit him on the nose. The lion lashed out with his paws. The gnat bit the lion's tail. The lion swung round, but now the gnat was on the beast's ear.

The lion became mad with rage, as the gnat bit him in a hundred places. At last, exhausted, the lion collapsed. The gnat buzzed around, boasting of his victory. He buzzed into a spider's web . . . and that was the end of him!

Complete the sentences.

a The gnat did not like the idea of the lion being _____ .

b The gnat boasted that he would be the _____ .

c When the lion was bitten on the _____, he lashed out with his paws.

d At last, the lion became _____ and collapsed.

e The gnat boasted of his _____.

f Having beaten the lion, the gnat ended his life in a _____ web.

___

Write the correct word under each picture.

_____   _____   _____   _____   _____

Mathematics 4

What time is it?

a [   ]   **b**  [   ]

c How many make ? [   ]

d How many make   ? [   ]

e What is the difference between and ? [   ]

f How much more do you need to make £1?   [   ]

How many days are there in the following months?

g March [   ]   **h** December [   ]   **i** June [   ]

j October [   ]   **k** April [   ]   **l** November [   ]

Write the answer in the box.

m 6 twos = [   ]   **n** 2 eights = [   ]   **o** 2 fives = [   ]

p 7 x 2 = [   ]   **q** 3 x 4 = [   ]   **r** 5 x 3 = [   ]

s Draw a line to join each shape to its name.

| oblong |
| circle |
| square |
| triangle |

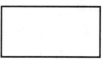

Language Skills 4

The following words are not in alphabetical order.
Write them below in alphabetical order.

a desk   television   chair   zoo

_____   _____   _____   _____

b pear   apple   orange   melon

_____   _____   _____   _____

c horse   cow   sheep   donkey

_____   _____   _____   _____

Complete the word under each picture by writing a vowel at the beginning.

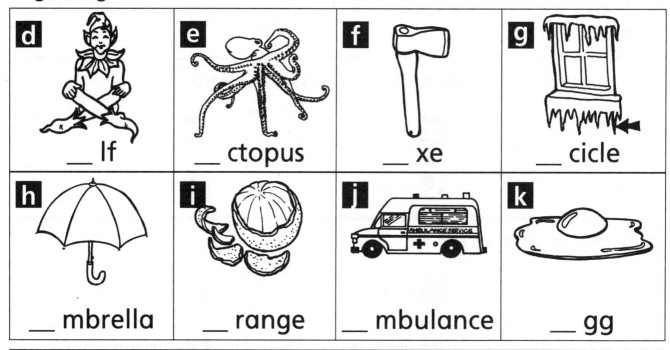

d __ lf   **e** __ ctopus   **f** __ xe   **g** __ cicle

h __ mbrella   **i** __ range   **j** __ mbulance   **k** __ gg

Each word below a picture should begin with **dr** or **tr**.
Complete each word by writing **dr** or **tr** on the line.

l __ ain   **m** __ aw   **n** __ uck   **o** __ olley   **p** __ um

page 22

All living things need food. Green plants make their own food. Animals cannot make their own food. They eat plants and other animals.

Write the names of these creatures below the pictures.

a

b

c

d

_____

e

f

g

h

_____

i

j

_____

k **Some animals eat plants only. Some animals eat other animals. Use the ten animals above to write two lists.**
In the first list write the animals that eat plants only. In the second list write the animals that eat other animals.

Eat only plants	Eat other animals
_____ _____	_____ _____
_____ _____	_____ _____
_____	_____

Writing 4

The special name of a person, place or thing begins with a capital letter.

On <u>M</u>onday <u>J</u>une drove to <u>L</u>ondon in her <u>M</u>ondeo.

Write out these sentences.
Use capital letters and full stops where they are needed.

a last christmas we had a big family party

_____

b auntie helen came from leeds

_____

c my cousins, joe and emma, were there

_____

d uncle melvin from wales gave me a video

_____

e the video was called robin hood

_____

f our dog chips got a new collar

_____

g we all had a wonderful christmas day

_____

Which pairs of words in the pictures are opposites?
Write the four pairs below the pictures.

| back | low | large | high |

  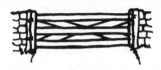

| small | narrow | front | wide |

a _____ and _____   _____ and _____

_____ and _____   _____ and _____

Fill in the missing numbers.

b 4 6 ___ 10 ___ 14   **c** 5 7 ___ 11 13 ___

d 5 10 15 ___ 25   **e** 30 25 ___ 15 ___

What do the people and the animal in the top row make in the second row of pictures? Finish the sentences below.

| carpenter | cow | builder | baker |

 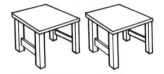 

| bread | tables | milk | houses |

f A carpenter makes _____ . A _____ makes milk.

A builder makes _____ .

A _____ makes _____ .

Our chocolate comes from the cocoa tree, which grows in several hot countries. On this tree grows the cocoa pod. Each pod contains a number of cocoa beans.

First the beans are removed from the pods and dried. Then, at the factory, they are cleaned, roasted and ground to a paste. This is pressed to take out most of the liquid, which is called cocoa butter. This leaves a pure cocoa block. When this is ground down it becomes cocoa powder.

To make sweet eating chocolate, the cocoa block is mixed with cocoa butter and sugar. Milk is added to make milk chocolate.

Complete the sentences.

a Cocoa beans grow in a cocoa _____ .

b When the beans are dried they are taken to a _____ .

c Before being ground to a paste, the beans are _____ and roasted.

d The paste is made into a cocoa block by pressing out most of the cocoa _____ .

e Sweet eating chocolate is made by mixing the cocoa block with cocoa butter and _____ .

f The cocoa tree grows in several _____ countries.

Underline the word which does not belong in each line.

g tea	cocoa	bread	coffee
h cake	jam	jar	chocolate
i large	tiny	enormous	huge
j hill	pond	river	lake
k pencil	paper	crayon	pen

Mathematics 5

a Draw two lines to divide the circle into four quarters.

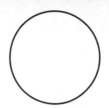

b A cake is cut into quarters. Jane, Tom and Owen each eat a quarter. How many quarters are left?

What is a quarter of each of the following?

c 4 [ ]

d 16 [ ]

e 8 [ ]

Write the answers in the boxes.

f 8 + 2 + 3 = [ ]

g 7 + [ ] = 12

h [ ] + 3 = 15

i 9 + 4 + 6 = [ ]

j 17 − 6 = [ ]

k 12 − [ ] = 9

l [ ] − 5 = 4

m 9 + 2 − 1 = [ ]

n A hexagon is any shape with six sides and six corners. Colour in all the hexagons.

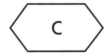

o 4 x 2 = [ ]

p 2 x 5 = [ ]

q 3 x 3 = [ ]

r 4 x 1 = [ ]

s 3 x 2 = [ ]

t 5 x 3 = [ ]

u 2 x 2 = [ ]

v 4 x 4 = [ ]

Schofield & Sims

Schofield & Sims was established in 1901 by two headmasters and since then our name has been synonymous with educationally sound texts and teaching materials. Our mission is to publish products which are:

- **Educationally sound** • **Good value** • **Written by experienced teachers**
  - **Extensively used in schools, nurseries and play groups**
  - **Used by parents to support their children's learning**

HOMEWORK 1

Exercises in reading and vocabulary, language skills, writing, mathematics, science and thinking. Suitable for use at home, with or without parental help. Each book includes an answer booklet.

Homework Book 1 - 978 07217 0845 4

Homework Book 2 - 978 07217 0846 1

Homework Book 3 - 978 07217 0851 5

Homework Book 4 - 978 07217 0852 2

Schofield & Sims Key Stage 2 products for 7 to 11 year olds

Language and literacy workbooks

Key Spellings
Books 1 - 4
Pattern and sound based spelling activities and exercises to establish basic spelling skills.

New Spellaway
Books 1 - 4
A progressive series complementing the formal teaching of spelling. New patterns are consolidated, through the 'look, say, cover, write, check' approach.

Springboard
Books 1 - 8 plus Introductory Book
English workbooks covering word construction, spelling, vocabulary, grammar, comprehension exercises and creative work. Age range 6 - 11.

Maths and numeracy workbooks

Mental Arithmetic
Books 1 - 6 plus Introductory Book
Covers essential mental maths skills through 36 carefully graded tests in each book along with progress tests and diagnostic tests. Supported by corresponding series of Teacher's Books.

Times Tables
Books 1 and 2
Straight forward tables practice.
Book 2 covers x6, x7, x8, x9, x11, x12 tables.
(Book 1 is for Key Stage 1)

Posters

Sturdy laminated posters, full colour, write-on/wipe-off, suitable for wall mounting or desk top use. Over 70 titles covering numeracy, literacy, science, nature, geography, history and languages.

Information

For further information about products for pre-school, Key Stages 1 and 2, please request our catalogue or visit our website at

www.schofieldandsims.co.uk

Author	Chris Burgess
Cover design	Curve Creative - Bradford

©1997 Schofield & Sims Ltd.

First printed 1998
Reprinted 1998 (twice), 1999 (three times), 2000, 2001 (twice), 2002, 2003, 2004 (twice), 2005, 2006 (twice), 2007

Printed by Wyndeham Gait Ltd., Grimsby

Schofield & Sims

Dogley Mill, Fenay Bridge, Huddersfield, HD8 0NQ
Phone 01484 607080   Fax 01484 606815

e-mail sales@schofieldandsims.co.uk

ISBN 978-07217-0845-4

9 780721 708454

Price £1.95
Key Stage 2
Age Range 7-11 years